THEN AND NOW
HOMES
THEN AND NOW

by Nadia Higgins

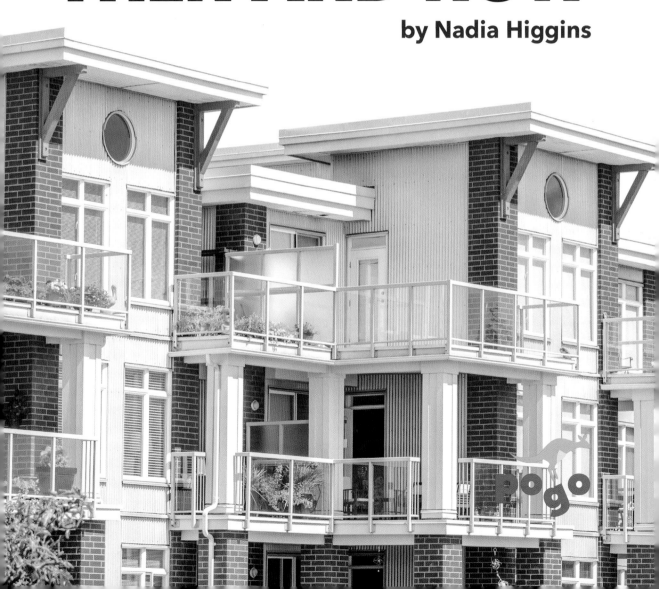

pogo

Ideas for Parents and Teachers

Pogo Books let children practice reading informational text while introducing them to nonfiction features such as headings, labels, sidebars, maps, and diagrams, as well as a table of contents, glossary, and index.

Carefully leveled text with a strong photo match offers early fluent readers the support they need to succeed.

Before Reading

- "Walk" through the book and point out the various nonfiction features. Ask the student what purpose each feature serves.

- Look at the glossary together. Read and discuss the words.

Read the Book

- Have the child read the book independently.

- Invite him or her to list questions that arise from reading.

After Reading

- Discuss the child's questions. Talk about how he or she might find answers to those questions.

- Prompt the child to think more. Ask: How do homes then and now differ? How are they the same? What makes your home unique?

Pogo Books are published by Jump!
5357 Penn Avenue South
Minneapolis, MN 55419
www.jumplibrary.com

Library of Congress Cataloging-in-Publication Data is available at www.loc.gov or upon request from the publisher.

ISBN: 978-1-64128-474-5 (hardcover)
ISBN: 978-1-64128-475-2 (paperback)
ISBN: 978-1-64128-476-9 (ebook)

Editor: Jenna Trnka
Designer: Molly Ballanger

Photo Credits: KBitto/Shutterstock, cover (left); karamysh/Shutterstock, cover (right); 1; Kamira/Shutterstock, 3; sumikophoto/Shutterstock, 4; GraphicaArtis/Getty, 5; John Greim/Age Fotostock/SuperStock, 6-7; Capture Light/Shutterstock, 8-9; JenniferPhotographyImaging/iStock, 10; Buyenlarge/Getty, 11; Rosemary Thornton, 12-13; ClassicStock.com/SuperStock, 14; tillsonburg/Getty, 15; Tom Sibley/Getty, 16-17; qingwa/iStock, 18-19; Westend61/Getty, 20-21; Denys Prykhodov/Shutterstock, 21 (tablet); Artazum/Shutterstock, 23.

Printed in the United States of America at Corporate Graphics in North Mankato, Minnesota.

TABLE OF CONTENTS

CHAPTER 1
Home Sweet Home 4

CHAPTER 2
Changing Spaces 10

CHAPTER 3
Modern Living 14

ACTIVITIES & TOOLS
Try This! 22
Glossary 23
Index 24
To Learn More 24

CHAPTER 1

HOME SWEET HOME

Homes provide shelter. They protect us from weather. More than 1,000 years ago, Native Americans in the southwest built homes with clay. These still stand today.

On the Great Plains, Native Americans built **tipis** out of buffalo skins. They could pack up and move these homes in a single day.

tipi

In the 1600s, a typical home was on a farm. It was small. Just one or two rooms. Without **electricity**, people used candles for light. And fireplaces for heat. They lugged water in from a well. As for bathrooms? **Outhouses** were outside.

WHAT DO YOU THINK?

Nearly everything used to happen at home. Births. School. Weddings. Clothes and tools were made at home, too. What activities do you do at home?

In the early 1800s, white settlers moved west. They built log cabins from the trees around them. Nails were hard to come by. So they carved notches into the logs. That way, the logs stayed stacked.

WHAT DO YOU THINK?

Few trees grow on the **prairie**. Here, settlers made **sod** houses. They cut out blocks of tough grass roots. Then they stacked the blocks. What materials do you think were used to build your home?

log
notches

CHAPTER 2

CHANGING SPACES

By the late 1800s, wood for building could be cut at a **lumber mill** instead of by hand. The railroad helped ship building materials across the country. Cities grew. Houses got bigger. And taller.

parlor

The **parlor** was a room just for hosting guests. Here, people showed off their finest things. Books. Art. Electric light bulbs. These were signs of wealth.

The country kept growing. In the early 1900s, more people needed homes. You could order a house, small or large, from a **catalog**.

Parts of the house were made in factories and shipped. Builders put it all together on the land. By the 1920s, these houses had indoor bathrooms and electricity.

catalog ·····▶

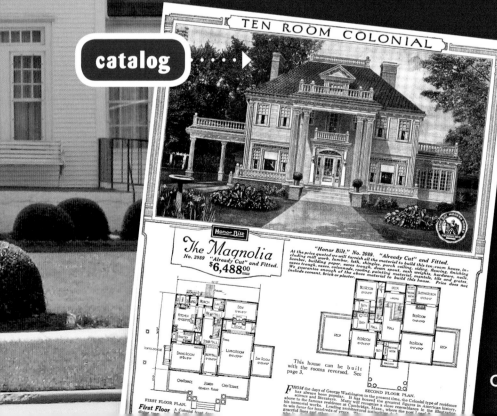

CHAPTER 3

MODERN LIVING

More families bought houses in the 1950s. The home became a place to relax. Everyone gathered in the family room to watch a new invention. What was it? TV!

1950s TV

Suburbs outside the city grew. There was space for yards. Garages, too.

In the city, high-rise apartments filled up. Some of these tall towers had 30 stories or more. You rode an elevator to your floor.

In the 1990s, **luxury** apartments had rooftop pools. Gyms. Coffee shops.

DID YOU KNOW?

A home does not have to stay in one spot. Mobile homes can drive around. Houseboats float on water. Astronauts live at the International Space Station. Their home orbits Earth every 90 minutes!

high-rise
apartment

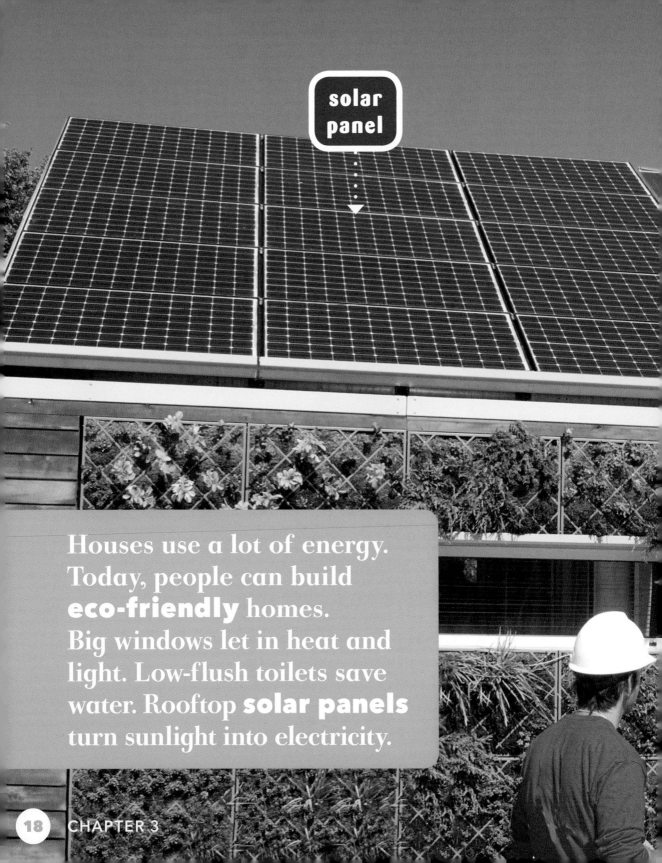

solar panel

Houses use a lot of energy. Today, people can build **eco-friendly** homes. Big windows let in heat and light. Low-flush toilets save water. Rooftop **solar panels** turn sunlight into electricity.

TAKE A LOOK!

A **floor plan** is like a map of a house. Take a look at this floor plan. Note its rooms. How are they laid out? What features do you see?

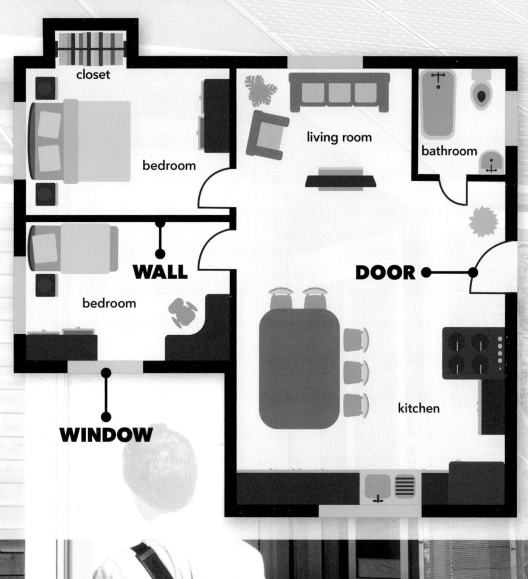

closet

bedroom

living room

bathroom

WALL

bedroom

DOOR

kitchen

WINDOW

Smart homes use Wi-Fi, cameras, and microphones to let you control anything that uses electricity. Walk into a room, and the lights come on. Tell your house, "Turn up the heat." Tap your phone to turn on the TV. What if your home were smart? What would you ask it to do?

ACTIVITIES & TOOLS

DRAW A FLOOR PLAN

Page 19 shows a floor plan. Draw one of your home!

What You Need:

- sheet of paper
- ruler
- pencil
- eraser
- markers or colored pencils

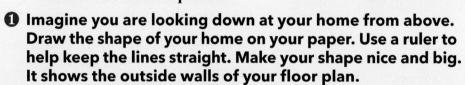

❶ Imagine you are looking down at your home from above. Draw the shape of your home on your paper. Use a ruler to help keep the lines straight. Make your shape nice and big. It shows the outside walls of your floor plan.

❷ If your home has two stories, start with the first floor. Think about where all of the rooms are. What rooms touch the outside wall? What rooms are next to each other? Draw the rooms inside your floor plan. Add labels.

❸ Next, add the doors, both inside and outside. Erase a little bit of the line to show where the doors are.

❹ Add in details. Draw where sinks, toilets, beds, and other things should be.

❺ After you've finished your floor plan, color it. Or start with a new sheet of paper to draw another floor if your home has more than one story.

❻ Show your floor plan to someone who lives with you. What do they think?

GLOSSARY

catalog: A magazine with pictures and descriptions of things you can buy.

eco-friendly: Not harmful to the environment.

electricity: Electrical power that is generated in special plants and distributed to all parts of the country.

floor plan: A layout or diagram of a room or floor of rooms as viewed from above.

lumber mill: A facility where logs are cut into lumber for building.

luxury: Expensive, comfortable, and elegant.

outhouses: Small outdoor buildings that are used as toilets.

parlor: A formal living room, especially in an old house, used for conversations with guests.

prairie: A large, flat area of land with rolling grassland and few or no trees.

smart homes: Homes equipped with lighting, heating, and electronic devices that can be controlled remotely by phone or computer.

sod: The top layer of soil and the grass that grows in it.

solar panels: Large, flat devices that use sunlight to create electricity.

suburbs: Areas close to the outer edges of cities that are made up mostly of homes.

tipis: Cone-shaped tents made from animal skins.

INDEX

apartments 16

catalog 13

eco-friendly homes 18

electricity 7, 13, 18, 21

factories 13

family room 14

farm 7

floor plan 19

garages 15

heat 7, 18, 21

houseboats 16

light 7, 11, 18, 21

log cabins 8

mobile homes 16

outhouses 7

parlor 11

railroad 10

room 7, 11, 13, 14, 19, 21

smart homes 21

sod houses 8

solar panels 18

suburbs 15

tipis 5

water 7, 16, 18

wood 10

yards 15

TO LEARN MORE

Finding more information is as easy as 1, 2, 3.

❶ Go to www.factsurfer.com

❷ Enter "homesthenandnow" into the search box.

❸ Click the "Surf" button to see a list of websites.

FACT SURFER